Supporting **Writing Skills**

FOR AGES 7–8

Andrew Brodie

Introduction

Supporting Writing Skills is aimed at all those who work with children who have been identified as needing 'additional' or 'different' literacy support. It can be used by anyone working with children who fall into this category, whether you are a teacher, classroom assistant or parent.

Typically the seven to eight year-old children for whom the book is intended will be working at the levels expected of Year 2 children or may simply need extra help in tackling the level of work appropriate for Year 3. Their difficulties may be short term, and can be overcome with extra practice and support on a one-to-one or small group basis, or they may be long term, where such support enables them to make progress but at a level behind their peer group.

The activities in this book provide exactly what these children need – plenty of writing activities linked to the work that they will be completing across the curriculum. All the activities provide great opportunities for speaking and listening and most pages include reading practice in addition to the main writing task. Each activity page includes brief teachers' notes so that the pages can be picked up and used quickly and effectively.

The 2006 Framework for teaching Literacy lists twelve strands for literacy development. Strands 1 to 4 concern Speaking and Listening; Strands 5 to 12 concern Reading and Writing. The writing activities in this book have been created to match many of the key elements of the Framework's reading and writing strands for Key Stage 1 and Year 3:

5. Special note: our activities reflect the move from word recognition to language comprehension but we recognise that some lower ability pupils will still need some support with decoding and encoding

6. Spell with increasing accuracy and confidence, drawing on word recognition and knowledge of word structure, and spelling patterns including common inflections and use of double letters; spell high and medium frequency words; spell unfamiliar words using known conventions including grapheme-phoneme correspondences and morphological rules

7. Extend their vocabulary, exploring the meanings and sounds of new words; show an understanding of the elements of stories, such as main character, sequence of events; explain organisational features of texts, including alphabetical order, layout, diagrams, captions

8. Show an understanding of the elements of stories, such as main character, sequence of events; empathise with characters

9. Use beginning, middle and end to write narratives in which events are sequenced logically and conflicts resolved; write non-narrative texts using structures of different text types; select and use a range of technical and descriptive vocabulary

10. Write chronological and non-chronological texts using simple structures; use planning to establish clear sections for writing

11. Write simple and compound sentences; compose sentences using tense consistently (present and past); use capital letters and full stops when punctuating simple sentences; use question marks, and use commas to separate items in a list

12. Write with consistency in the size and proportion of letters and spacing within and between words, using the correct formation of handwriting joins.

Children generally achieve the greatest success in an atmosphere of support and encouragement. Praise from a caring adult can be the best reward for the children's efforts. The worksheets and activities in this book will provide many opportunities for children to enjoy these successes. The development of a positive attitude and the resulting increase in self-esteem will help them with all of their schoolwork.

This book consists of three main sections:

Section 1 (pages 6–29)

Worksheets 1 to 23 contain activities to encourage the process of spelling new words, including some that will be needed for work across the curriculum, through use of phonic skills. The worksheets provide many opportunities for creating simple sentences then more complex sentences. Sentences with clear punctuation are modelled for the pupils then the activities promote the construction of accurate sentences that start with capital letters and end with full stops. Some pages require pupils to write just one sentence, using relevant vocabulary, while others require several sentences on a particular theme.

Several pages include dictation exercises. These help children both to identify the sounds in particular words to assist with their spelling and to 'hear' the punctuation. By listening carefully to the sentences dictated by the teacher the children can spot where to use full stops, commas or question marks.

Section 2 (pages 31–47)

With two sets of narrative sheets, pupils are encouraged to work out the correct sequence of a set of paragraphs and to combine these with the images provided. From this speaking, listening and reading activity the children move on to rewriting the text within a simple 'book' presentation. Further templates are provided to enable the children to create independent texts.

Section 3 (pages 51–64)

An important resource contained within this book is the dictionary that can be created from the final fourteen sheets. This contains all the high frequency words recommended for KS1, together with all the additional words used in this book. We suggest that you complete Worksheets 2 to 5, which provide practice of the alphabet, before creating this resource. The dictionary can be used by the children when working on the worksheets.

Each page of the dictionary has spaces for pupils to write their own spellings – this is an excellent way of encouraging the children to use their phonic knowledge to spell new words. When a child needs a word, help her/him to find the correct page of the dictionary then ask her/him to attempt the word by segmenting it into its phonemes. Give the child lots of praise where s/he is successful even in part of a word then write the word correctly on the line next to her/his attempt, stressing the phonemes and pointing out the graphemes that represent these.

Contents

Worksheet/title	Speaking and Listening strand	Reading and Writing strand	
Record and Review			page 5

Section 1

Worksheet/title	Speaking and Listening strand	Reading and Writing strand	
1 All about me	1 2 3	5 6 9 10 11 12	page 6
2 The lower case alphabet	2 3	5 6 12	page 7
3 The upper case alphabet	2 3	5 6 12	page 8
4 Names in your class	1 2 3	5 6 12	page 9
5 Matching lower case and upper case	2 3	5 6 12	page 10
6 What I did today	1 2 3	5 6 7 9 10 11 12	page 11
7 Describe your morning	1 2 3	5 6 9 10 11 12	page 12
8 Where do you live?	1 2 3	5 6 7 9 10 11 12	page 13
9 Asking questions	1 2 3 4	5 6 7 9 10 11 12	page 14
10 Asking more questions	1 2 3 4	5 6 7 9 10 11 12	page 15
11 What were the questions?	1 2 3	5 6 7 9 10 11 12	page 16
12 Favourite things	1 2 3	5 6 9 10 11 12	page 17
13 Your favourite things	1 2 3	5 6 9 10 11 12	page 18
14 Days and months	1 2 3	5 6 12	page 19
15 Words for numbers 1	2 3	5 6 12	page 20
16 Words for numbers 2	2 3	5 6 12	page 21
17 January, February, March	2 3	5 6 9 10 11 12	page 23
18 April, May, June	2 3	5 6 9 10 11 12	page 24
19 July, August, September	2 3	5 6 9 10 11 12	page 25
20 October, November, December	2 3	5 6 9 10 11 12	page 26
21 Labelling a face	1 2 3	5 6 12	page 27
22 Teeth	1 2 3	5 6 9 10 11 12	page 28
23 North, South, East and West	1 2 3	5 6 9 10 11 12	page 29

Section 2

Worksheet/title	Speaking and Listening strand	Reading and Writing strand	
Teachers' notes for pages 31–38			page 30
The Lion and the Mouse	1 2 3	5 6 7 8 9 10 11 12	pages 31–37
The Lion and the Mouse comprehension	1 2 3	5 6 7 8 9 10 11 12	page 38
Teachers' notes for pages 40–47			page 39
The Owl, Cat and Mouse	1 2 3	5 6 7 8 9 10 11 12	pages 40–46
The Owl, Cat and Mouse comprehension	1 2 3	5 6 7 8 9 10 11 12	page 47
Writing templates	1 2 3	5 6 10 11 12	pages 48–49

Section 3

Worksheet/title	Speaking and Listening strand	Reading and Writing strand	
Teachers' notes for the Dictionary resource sheets			page 50
Dictionary resource sheets	1 2 3	5 6 12	pages 51–64

Record and Review

Name: _____ Date of birth: _____

Teacher: _____ Class: _____

Support assistant: _____

Code of Practice stage: _____ Date targets set: _____

Target

1 _____

2 _____

3 _____

4 _____

Review

Target

1 _____

_____

Target achieved? ☐ Date: _____

2 _____

_____

Target achieved? ☐ Date: _____

3 _____

_____

Target achieved? ☐ Date: _____

4 _____

_____

Target achieved? ☐ Date: _____

Name: _____ **Date:** _____

My full name: _____

My date of birth: _____

My address:

_____

_____

_____

_____

_____

Draw a picture of yourself.

My school: _____

_____

My teachers: _____

_____

Things I like: _____

_____

_____

Things I don't like: _____

_____

Notes for teachers
This worksheet provides lots of opportunities for getting to know a new pupil. Discuss each category before helping her/him to fill in the details. S/he may not know her/his own address or date of birth. It would be a good idea to have these details ready so that you can help to provide the information. Some of the spellings can be found in the dictionary created from the Resource sheets on pages 51–64. Other new words can be entered in the dictionary by the child, with your help.

Name: **Date:**

Here is the alphabet, written in lower case letters.

a b c d e f g h i j k l m n o p q r s t u v w x y z

My name, Owl, begins with a vowel.

Which letters are vowels? _____

Write the tall letters. _____

Write the letters that pass through the line. _____

Now write all the other letters. _____

_____

Use neat handwriting to write out the whole alphabet.
Leave spaces between the letters.

_____

_____

Notes for teachers
Children need lots of opportunities to speak and to listen before they can become effective writers. Discuss the alphabet with the child, saying the names of the letters and the sounds that they make. Look at the owl's speech bubble. Ask the child why 'Owl' is written with a capital O. Discuss the fact that Owl and vowel rhyme but that they are spelt quite differently. Read the question sentence and the instruction sentences with the child. Encourage her/him to notice that the question sentence ends with a question mark. Ensure that the child writes the letters in a style appropriate to the school's handwriting policy. Stress the importance of the descenders going through the line, paying particular attention to the letter j which many children write incorrectly.

Name: _____

Date: _____

Here is the alphabet, written in upper case letters.

A B C D E F G H I J K L M N O P Q R S T U V W X Y Z

Upper case letters are called capital letters.
Everybody's name starts with a capital letter.

Look at all these names.

Tariq Amy Xanthe Kim Mike Nigel Quentin Will Gaby Fazal Zoe Leo Holly Ben Chloe Dave Usha Ivy Yasmin Rebecca Pete Vinny Octavia Jack Elvin Sam

Write the names in alphabetical order.

_____   _____   _____

_____   _____   _____

_____   _____   _____

_____   _____   _____

_____   _____   _____

_____   _____   _____

_____   _____   _____

Notes for teachers

Discuss the alphabet with the child, saying the names of the letters and the sounds that they make and explaining that capital letters are sometimes called upper case letters. Read all the sentences with the child then help her/him to read the names. Most of the names follow simple phonetic patterns and can be read by blending the phonemes. Make sure that the child copies the names accurately and that s/he remembers that each one needs a capital letter at the start.

Andrew Brodie: Supporting Writing Skills © A & C Black Publishers Ltd. 2007

Name: **Date:**

Here is the alphabet, written in upper case letters.

A B C D E F G H I J K L M N O P Q R S T U V W X Y Z

Upper case letters are called capital letters.
Everybody's name starts with a capital letter.

Can you find the first names of everybody in your class?
Write all the names here.

Notes for teachers
Discuss the alphabet with the child, saying the names of the letters and the sounds that they make and explaining that capital letters are sometimes called upper case letters. Read all the sentences with the child, pointing out that one sentence ends with a question mark because it is a question. Help the child to find the names of people in the class. If you feel that the child cannot cope with too many names just take a selection but if the child is able to do so, try to produce the whole class list. If the child is capable of doing so, s/he could write the names in alphabetical order on a separate piece of paper. Arranging these in alphabetical order will be more difficult than the process on Worksheet 3 as some letters of the alphabet will not have names to match them and others will have several names. Help the child as s/he goes through the alphabet asking questions such as: "Are there any names beginning with A?" "How can we put those in order?" "Are there any names beginning with B?" Etc.

Name:

Date:

How quickly can you join the pairs of letters?

Draw a line to connect the **a** to the **A**, then another

line to join the **b** to the **B** and so on.

Time yourself.

h o B p W j P

C S f I i b c

v t L Q G X

D k A m s

l z u K N U

Y q r

Z x R g J H e

w

F T n V d

y E O a M

Notes for teachers

Revise the alphabet with the child, saying the names of the letters and the sounds that they make. Help her/him to draw lines to join the lower case letters to the matching upper case letters. Make sure the child completes the activity in alphabetical order. Set the challenge of completing the task as quickly as possible. This activity can be repeated several times as it encourages the child to practise alphabetical order. It is essential that s/he can recognise the capital letter equivalent of each lower case letter. Take the opportunity to introduce the dictionary created from the Resource sheets on pages 51–64. A further time challenge that can be set for the child will be to see how quickly s/he can locate a particular page in this dictionary e.g. How quickly can s/he find the **k** page, the **p** page, the **m** page, etc?

     Andrew Brodie: Supporting Writing Skills © A & C Black Publishers Ltd. 2007

worksheet **6**

WORD BANK

alarm seven o'clock shower dressed downstairs
breakfast cereal locked front door drove school

This is what I did today.

Notes for teachers

You may decide to cut off the teacher's notes on this worksheet as you will need to read some sentences to the child while s/he is writing. This dictation exercise provides the opportunity for you to model how the child could describe her/his morning (a task that s/he completes on Worksheet 7). Discuss the pictures and the words in the word bank with the child then dictate the following sentences slowly and carefully:

I woke up when the alarm went off at seven o'clock.
I had a shower and got dressed then I went downstairs.
For breakfast I had some cereal and a drink.
After breakfast I locked the front door then drove to school in the car.

You may need to repeat each sentence several times, helping the child to segment the words into phonemes to be able to spell them. Encourage the child to write neatly, following the school's handwriting policy, and to start each sentence with a capital letter and to end it with a full stop.

Andrew Brodie: Supporting Writing Skills © A & C Black Publishers Ltd. 2007

Name: _____ **Date:** _____

Describe your morning.

Notes for teachers
Help the child to read the instruction sentence. Point out that it starts with a capital letter because all sentences do and that it ends with a full stop. Discuss ideas with the child to help her/him to think of what s/he does in the morning. Show her/him the completed Worksheet 6 to provide a reminder of some of the spellings but, more importantly, to give ideas for the child's own sentences. When s/he is ready help her/him to show the time s/he woke up on the clock face. Encourage her/him to draw a picture related to her/his writing about the morning's activities.

Answer the questions. Use full sentences for your answers. Don't forget that you need a capital letter at the start of each sentence and a full stop at the end.

Where do you live?

_____

_____

Do you live in a house, a flat, a bungalow or a caravan?

_____

_____

Do you have any pets at home?

_____

_____

Do you have a garden? If you do, what is it like?

_____

_____

Notes for teachers

If possible, find a microphone and conduct a mock television interview asking the child the questions on the worksheet before showing them to her/him. Help the child to read the instructions and then the question sentences. Point out that each sentence starts with a capital letter because all sentences do and that all the question sentences end with question marks. Help the child to compose a full reply to each sentence, encouraging her/him to plan the whole sentence before writing it down. This will be an easier task if you have been able to conduct the mock interview. This sheet provides an introduction to Worksheets 9 and 10 where the child is asked to write his/her own questions.

Andrew Brodie: Supporting Writing Skills © A & C Black Publishers Ltd. 2007

Write some questions of your own.

Don't forget that every question starts with a capital letter.

Don't forget that every question ends with a question mark.

Notes for teachers

Discuss the picture with the child and again, if possible, supply a microphone to encourage her/him to think of some questions to ask you. S/he may find it easier to compose some questions and write them down before you conduct a mock interview together, this time with the child asking the questions. You could remind her/him of the questions that appeared on Worksheet 8. S/he could use some or all of these or could make up new questions.

Write some questions for someone your age.

Don't forget that every question starts with a capital letter.

Don't forget that every question ends with a question mark.

Name: **Date:**

Read the sentences below. They are the replies to some questions. Try to work out what the questions were.

Q _____

A I'm very well thank you.

Q _____

A My favourite colour is green.

Q _____

A Yes, I have one brother and one sister.

Q _____

A Yes, I have a cat and a dog.

Q _____

A Beans on toast.

Q _____

A Apple juice.

Notes for teachers

Read through the sentences with the child, pointing out that they all start with capital letters and end with full stops. Explain that **Q** and **A** are short forms of writing _question_ and _answer_. Help the child to work out what each question could have been. The first few are very obvious but the last two are less so e.g. the reply _beans on toast_ could have resulted from: What is your favourite food? What did you have for tea last night? Etc.

WORD BANK

favourite	colours
fruit	cricket
juice	football
vegetables	tennis

These are a few of my favourite things.

My favourite colours are blue, red and green.

Now listen to your teacher and write the sentences.

Notes for teachers

You may decide to cut off the teacher's notes on this worksheet as you will need to read some sentences to the child while s/he is writing. This dictation exercise provides an opportunity for you to model how the child can use commas in lists. Help the child to read the speech bubble then discuss the 'colours sentence'. Point out that it starts with a capital letter and ends with a full stop but that it also has a comma. Explain that the comma is there because there are three items in a list and instead of saying 'blue and red and green' we can use a comma between the first two items. When you feel that the child is ready, dictate the following sentences one at a time.

I like to play cricket, football and tennis.
My favourite foods are bread, fruit and vegetables.
I like drinking milk, tea or apple juice.

You may need to repeat each sentence several times, helping the child to find words from the word bank and segmenting some of the other words into phonemes to be able to spell them. Encourage the child to write neatly, following the school's handwriting policy, and to start each sentence with a capital letter and to end it with a full stop.

Name: **Date:**

Draw yourself next to the
speech bubble.

> These are a few
> of my favourite
> things.

Can you write about your favourite things?

_____

_____

_____

_____

_____

_____

_____

_____

_____

_____

Notes for teachers

This activity sheet follows on from Worksheet 12. As an initial speaking and listening activity encourage the child to think about favourite things in several categories, e.g. food, drink, films, songs, animals, colours, games, etc. Support her/him in writing down the spellings of some of these items in the dictionary that can be created from the Resource sheets on pages 51–64. Encourage her/him to segment the words into their phonemes to help with the spelling process. Now ask her/him to write a sentence for each category. If the category has more than two items remind the child to use commas between the words except between the last two where s/he can use the word *and*.

Name: _____   **Date:** _____

Copy the names of the days and the names of the months.

Monday _____

Tuesday _____

Wednesday _____

Thursday _____

Friday _____

Saturday _____

Sunday _____

January _____   July _____

February _____   August _____

March _____   September _____

April _____   October _____

May _____   November _____

June _____   December _____

Notes for teachers

This sheet provides practice in reading and spelling the names of the days of the week and the months of the year. These words are also shown on the back page of the dictionary created from the Resource sheets on pages 51–64. The names of the months will be needed for completing Worksheets 17 to 20. Point out to the child that the names of every day and every month start with capital letters. You may like to focus on the spelling of *February*. Help the child to say it correctly, *Feb-ru-a-ry* (phonemes /f/, /e/, /b/, /r/, /ue/, /e/, /r/, /ee/), where the first letter r is sounded clearly.

Name: _____ **Date:** _____

WORD BANK

one nine thirty two four fifty five twelve

forty six eight ten eleven ninety sixteen

thirteen seven eighty fifteen seventeen

eighteen three seventy nineteen twenty

fourteen sixty hundred

Write the words for the numbers.

1 _____   11 _____   30 _____

2 _____   12 _____   40 _____

3 _____   13 _____   50 _____

4 _____   14 _____   60 _____

5 _____   15 _____   70 _____

6 _____   16 _____   80 _____

7 _____   17 _____   90 _____

8 _____   18 _____   100 _____

9 _____   19 _____

10 _____   20 _____

Notes for teachers

This sheet provides practice in reading and spelling the names of numbers from one to twenty and the multiples of ten up to one hundred. As it is purely a spelling task and the child is not asked to write complete sentences, you could take the opportunity to ensure that s/he is forming letters correctly in accordance with the school's handwriting policy. You could draw attention to the spellings of 4, 14 and 40. Does the child notice that the letter *u* is not needed in the word *forty*?

 Andrew Brodie: Supporting Writing Skills © A & C Black Publishers Ltd. 2007

Name: _____ **Date:** _____

Write the words for the numbers.
The first four have been done for you.

11	eleven	35	_____
21	twenty-one	85	_____
31	thirty-one	16	_____
41	forty-one	46	_____
12	_____	56	_____
22	_____	76	_____
42	_____	17	_____
72	_____	37	_____
13	_____	67	_____
33	_____	87	_____
53	_____	18	_____
83	_____	28	_____
14	_____	78	_____
24	_____	98	_____
64	_____	19	_____
94	_____	39	_____
15	_____	49	_____
25	_____	59	_____

Notes for teachers

This sheet provides practice in reading and spelling the names of numbers from eleven to twenty together with random double-digit numbers between twenty-one and ninety-eight. Point out the use of hyphens in numbers such as *twenty-one*, *thirty-one*, etc. As this is purely a spelling task and the child is not asked to write complete sentences, you could take the opportunity to ensure that s/he is forming letters correctly in accordance with the school's handwriting policy.

Teacher's notes for Worksheets 17 to 20

These worksheets provide opportunities to:

- practise spelling the names of the months of the year
- segment words into their phonemes to help with their spelling
- listen carefully to dictated sentences, hearing the effect of the punctuation
- draw on knowledge of previous texts to be able to punctuate simple sentences with capital letters, full stops and commas where appropriate

For each worksheet, dictate the sentences one at a time, slowly and carefully. For most months we have included three sentences but you may decide to use just two of them if the child finds writing particularly difficult. Support the child in segmenting the words into their phonemes or in looking them up in the dictionary created from the Dictionary resource sheets on pages 51–64. The child could also make use of Worksheet 14 to find the spellings of individual months and Worksheets 15 and 16 to find the spellings of numbers. Note that the numbers should be written in words rather than digits. Remind her/him that each sentence should start with a capital letter and end with a full stop and that the names of the months of the year always start with capital letters.

Although you will need to dictate some words individually, one of the key elements of dictation is the use of intonation to demonstrate the punctuation of complete sentences. Children can hear where the sentence starts, where commas appear and where the sentence ends. This acute listening experience will contribute greatly to the child's ability to punctuate her/his own work.

Dictation sentences for Worksheet 17

January is the first month of the year. It has thirty-one days. It is a winter month.

The second month of the year is February. Most years it has twenty-eight days but every four years it has twenty-nine days. These special years are called leap years.

The third month is March. It has thirty-one days. Spring starts in March.

Dictation sentences for Worksheet 18

April is the fourth month of the year. Flowers come out and leaves are growing on the trees. April has thirty days.

The fifth month of the year is May. May has thirty-one days.

June is the sixth month of the year. It has thirty days. June is in the summer and every day it does not go dark until late in the evening.

Dictation sentences for Worksheet 19

July is the seventh month of the year. It is time for the summer holidays. July has thirty-one days.

The eighth month is August. August has thirty-one days. Lots of people go on holiday.

September is the ninth month of the year. It has thirty days. Autumn starts in September.

Dictation sentences for Worksheet 20

October is the tenth month of the year. It is in the autumn. It has thirty-one days.

The eleventh month of the year is November. November only has thirty days. Bonfire night takes place in November.

The last month of the year is December. It goes dark very early every day. Winter starts in December. It has thirty-one days.

Name: _____ **Date:** _____

Listen carefully to your teacher.

Listen carefully to your teacher.

_____

_____

_____

_____

_____

_____

_____

_____

_____

_____

_____

_____

_____

_____

_____

_____

_____

Name: _____   **Date:** _____

Listen carefully to your teacher.

_____
_____
_____
_____
_____
_____
_____

_____
_____
_____
_____

_____
_____
_____
_____
_____
_____

Name:

Date:

Listen carefully to your teacher.

_____

Can you label the picture?

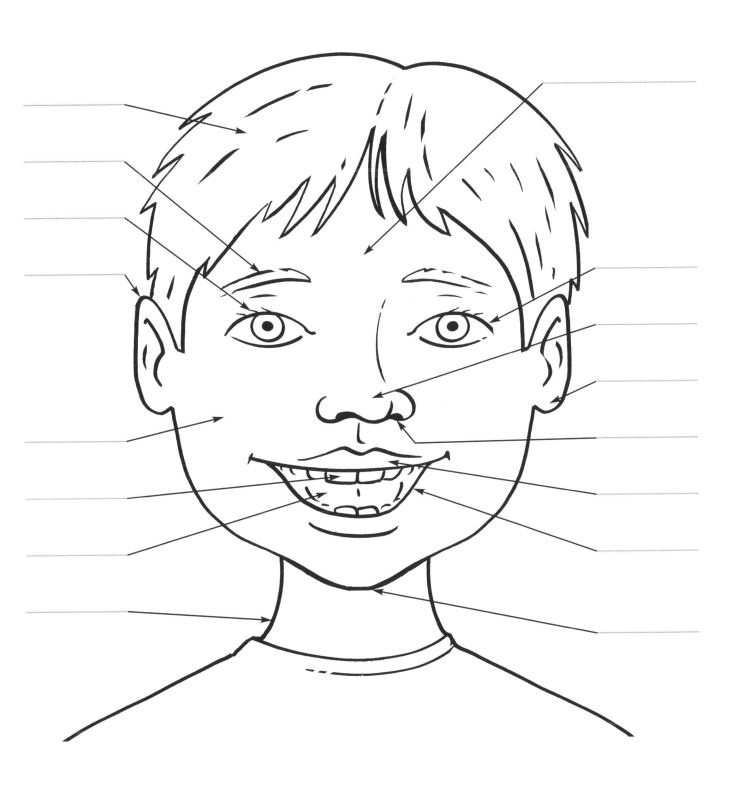

Notes for teachers
This worksheet provides excellent practice in using both phonic skills and the dictionary created from the Resource sheets on pages 51–64. Discuss the facial features with the child and encourage her/him to complete the labels. S/he could choose to look up the words in the dictionary or to attempt to segment the words into their phonemes and hence into their graphemes. Hopefully s/he will use a combination of the two methods.

Andrew Brodie: Supporting Writing Skills © A & C Black Publishers Ltd. 2007

27

Name: **Date:**

This picture is labelled for you.

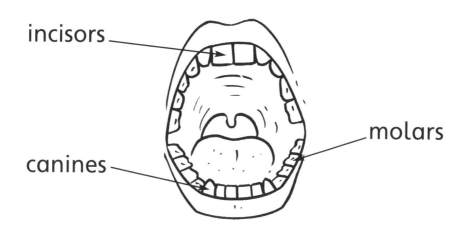

incisors

canines

molars

Listen to your teacher. Write the sentences

Notes for teachers

This worksheet provides practice in the vocabulary associated with the science topic on human teeth and eating.
Dictate the following sentences for the child to write down:

Incisors are at the front of the mouth and are used for cutting food.

Canines are next to the incisors and are used for tearing food.

Molars are near the back of the mouth and are used for chewing food.

If the child is confident, you may like to ask her/him to write about her/his own teeth. S/he could count the number of teeth in her/his own mouth and perhaps the number of each type, then make up some sentences e.g. I have twenty-eight teeth. There are fourteen at the top and fourteen at the bottom. Eight of my teeth are incisors. Four of my teeth are canines.

Andrew Brodie: Supporting Writing Skills © A & C Black Publishers Ltd. 2007

Write the words in
the correct places.

WORD BANK

East   North   South   West

England   Northern Ireland

Scotland   Wales

Answer the questions. Use full sentences for your answers.

Which country do you live in?

Do you live in the North, South, West or East of
the country?

What are the names of the other three countries
of the United Kingdom?

Notes for teachers

This worksheet provides practice in the vocabulary associated with geography and the four countries of the United
Kingdom. Encourage the child to write their answers using full sentences. Note that s/he will need to use a comma to
answer the third question. Help her/him to answer the final question. S/he may not have visited any other countries and
can compose an appropriate sentence. S/he may have visited other countries and could attempt to add their names to the
dictionary created from the Resource sheets on pages 51–64.

Notes for teachers on Worksheets 24 to 31

The next seven sheets feature the well-known fable of the lion and the mouse by the Greek writer Aesop. The pages will help the child to begin to create a piece of writing in a narrative form, possibly over several lessons.

Worksheets 24–28

The first four sheets each feature two pictures. (Note that one of the pictures forms the title page for the narrative story.) These sheets should be photocopied then cut in two so that the pictures can be introduced to the child one at a time and not necessarily in the correct order. In each case ask the child what the picture shows. The discussion of this picture is an excellent speaking and listening activity. Praise the child for finding all the details in the picture.

Having discussed the pictures, photocopy and cut out the seven pieces of writing on Worksheet 28. Read these with the child, then help her/him to match them to the pictures to make a story. This sequencing activity provides opportunities for lots of speaking and listening as well as considerable reading practice.

Worksheets 29–31

Photocopy Worksheets 29 and 30 back to back on to a single sheet. This can then be folded to make a simple four-page book. Help the child to write sentences to go with the pictures on each page of their book. The child could simply copy the paragraphs that s/he has sequenced or you could help her/him to compose sentences. If this is the case, help her/him to segment the words into their phonemes in order to spell them.

All of Aesop's fables that concerned animals had morals that could be related to humans. The moral of this fable illustrates the fact that sometimes a weak person may be helpful to a strong person. Worksheet 31 consists of a comprehension sheet in relation to the Lion and the Mouse story.

Andrew Brodie: Supporting Writing Skills © A & C Black Publishers Ltd. 2007

The Lion and the Mouse

One day a huge lion was sleeping quietly.
A mouse came along and ran over the lion's face.

The lion woke up and gave a loud roar.
He caught the mouse by the tail.

"Please don't kill me," said the mouse. "I will help you one day."

"How can you help me?" asked the lion, laughing. He let the mouse go anyway.

A few days later the lion got caught in a net.
He roared loudly.

The mouse heard the roar and went to help the lion.
He began to chew through the ropes.

At last the lion was able to get out of the net. "Thank you," said the lion, "you did help me as you said you would."

The Lion and the Mouse

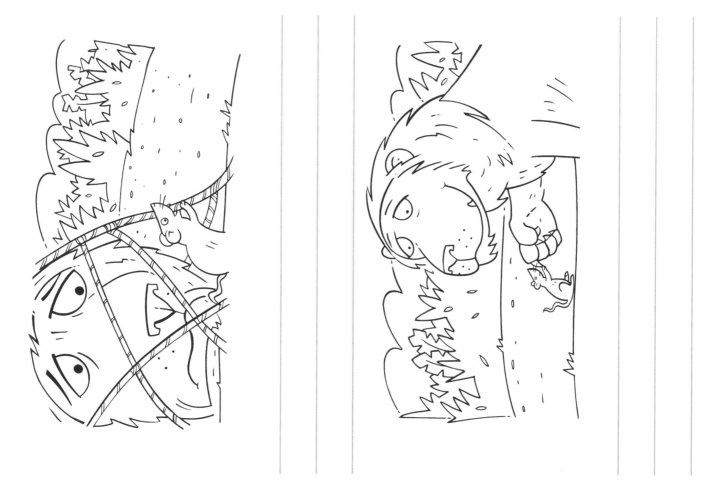

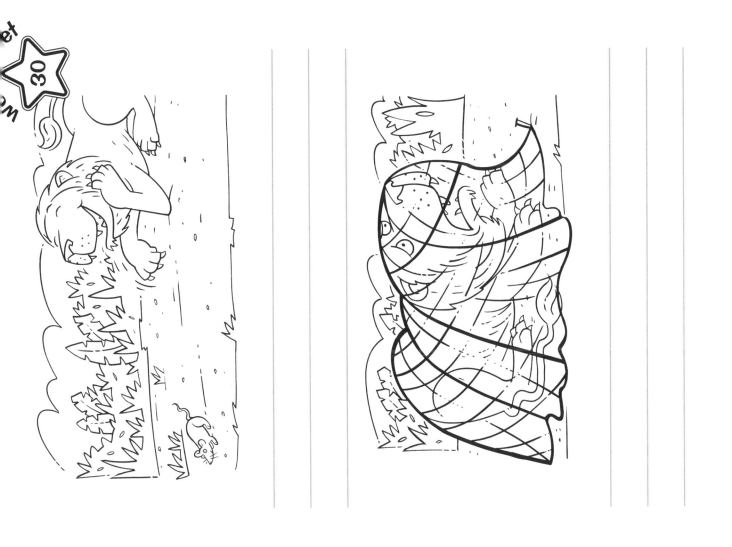

Name: Date:

Answer these questions about The lion and the mouse.

1 What made the lion wake up?

2 Why did the lion laugh at the mouse?

3 What happened to the lion?

4 How did the mouse help the lion?

5 Do you think a mouse could really help a lion in this way?

6 What do you think is the moral of the story?

Notes for teachers
Help the child to read the questions, then to compose answers orally before writing them down. Encourage the child to write complete sentences, remembering to start each one with a capital letter and to end it with a full stop. Discourage the child from starting her/his answer with the word 'because'. Help her/him to understand that the sentence has to make complete sense on its own as if the question is not there. Questions 5 and 6 are likely to be the most difficult as the child will not be able to find the answers simply from the story.

Andrew Brodie: Supporting Writing Skills © A & C Black Publishers Ltd. 2007

Notes for teachers on Worksheets 32 to 39 and the Writing templates

The next seven worksheets feature a simple story that has been adapted from an Indian fable written by the poet Somadeva nearly one thousand years ago.

Worksheets 32–36

The first four sheets each feature two pictures. (Note that one of the pictures forms the title page for the narrative story.) These sheets should be photocopied then cut in two so that the pictures can be introduced to the child one at a time and not necessarily in the correct order. In each case ask the child what the picture shows. The discussion of this picture is an excellent speaking and listening activity. Praise the child for finding all the details in the picture.

Having discussed the pictures, photocopy and cut out the seven short paragraphs shown on Worksheet 36. Read these with the child, then help her/him to match them to the pictures to make a story. This sequencing activity provides opportunities for lots of speaking and listening as well as considerable reading practice. The correct order of the paragraphs is as shown on Worksheet 36.

Worksheets 37–38

Photocopy Worksheets 37 and 38 back to back on to a single sheet. This can then be folded to make a simple four-page book. Help the child to write sentences to go with the pictures on each page of their book. The child could simply copy the paragraphs that s/he has sequenced or you could help her/him to compose their own sentences, telling the story in her/his own words, perhaps in a more simple style.

The moral of the fable concerns the fact that sometimes an enemy may become a friend but that friendship may not be a true friendship.

Worksheet 39 consists of a comprehension sheet in relation to the story.

Writing templates

Writing template 1 can be used for creating a four-page or eight-page book on any subject at any time. Simply photocopy this sheet on to both sides of a sheet of A4 paper then fold it to make a book, or use two sheets of A4 paper to make an eight-page book.

Writing template 2 can be photocopied to make a one-page A4 story sheet, again to be used at any time that you would like the child to produce a narrative or non-narrative piece of writing. The child can draw a picture at the top of the sheet and use the writing lines to write their own story.

The Owl, the Cat and the Mouse

Name: **Date:**

Andrew Brodie: Supporting Writing Skills © A & C Black Publishers Ltd. 2007

Name: _____   **Date:** _____

```
[                                                                    ]
[                                                                    ]
[                                                                    ]
[                                                                    ]
```

```
[                                                                    ]
[                                                                    ]
[                                                                    ]
[                                                                    ]
```

Lots of animals lived in one tree. An owl lived in a hole near the top of the tree. A cat lived in some branches halfway up. A tiny mouse lived in the roots.

One night the cat went out to hunt for food. He looked around carefully with his big eyes. The owl was out hunting too so the mouse had to hide from both of them.

Suddenly the moon went behind some clouds. It was very dark and the cat did not see a trap. His foot was caught in the trap and he could not escape.

The mouse came along and saw the cat caught in the trap. He was so happy but then he saw the owl swooping down.

"If you help me I will protect you from the owl," said the cat. "I will bite through the rope that is trapping you. But you must promise not to chase me ever again," said the mouse. "I promise," said the cat.

The mouse began biting through the rope and the owl flew away because he was afraid of the cat.
"Hurry up," said the cat.
"I am chewing as fast as I can," said the mouse. But he did not trust the cat so really he chewed very slowly.

When morning came and the owl had gone home to sleep, the mouse saw a man coming towards them. He knew that the cat was afraid of men so he chewed quickly to break the rope. The cat ran away from the man so the mouse was safe to run back to his hole in the roots of the tree.

Name: **Date:**

Answer the questions about The owl, the cat and the mouse.

1 Where did the owl, the cat and the mouse live?

2 How did the cat get caught?

3 What did the cat promise to the mouse?

4 Did the mouse believe the cat?

5 Who was the mouse afraid of?

6 Who was the cat afraid of?

7 Who was the owl afraid of?

Notes for teachers
Help the child to read the questions and to compose answers orally before writing them down. Encourage her/him to write complete sentences, remembering to start each one with a capital letter and to end it with a full stop. If the child has completed both stories, the Lion and the Mouse and the Owl, the Cat and the Mouse, you may like to discuss how the morals of the stories are different.

Writing template 1

Writing template 2

Notes for teachers on the Dictionary resource sheets

The dictionary that can be created from the final fourteen pages of this book is a very valuable resource. Photocopy the sheets to create master copies. Now photocopy the master copies, back to back, as follows:

Sheets 1/ 2   Sheets 3/4   Sheets 5/6   Sheets 7/8   Sheets 9/10   Sheets 11/12   Sheets 13/14

The dictionary contains all the high frequency words recommended for KS1, together with many of the additional words used in other books in this series.

Each page of the dictionary has spaces for pupils to write their own spellings. This is an excellent way of encouraging children to use their phonic knowledge to spell new words. When a child needs a word, help her/him to find the correct page of the dictionary, then ask her/him to attempt the word by segmenting it into its phonemes. Give the child lots of praise where s/he is successful even with part of a word, then write the word correctly on the line next to her/his attempt, stressing the phonemes and pointing out the graphemes that represent these.

Dictionary

Name

Days

Monday
Tuesday
Wednesday
Thursday
Friday
Saturday
Sunday

Months

January
February
March
April
May
June
July
August
September
October
November
December

Numbers

1   one
2   two
3   three
4   four
5   five
6   six
7   seven
8   eight
9   nine
10 ten
11 eleven
12 twelve
13 thirteen
14 fourteen
15 fifteen
16 sixteen
17 seventeen
18 eighteen
19 nineteen
20 twenty

Dictionary resource sheet 2

Name _____

Address _____

The alphabet

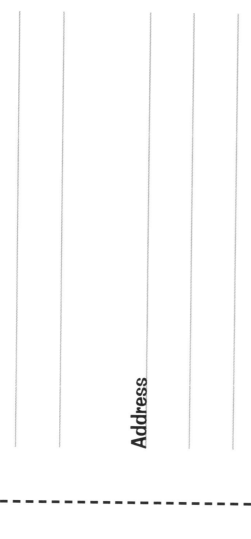

a A   n N

b B   o O

c C   p P

d D   q Q

e E   r R

f F   s S

g G   t T

h H   u U

i I   v V

j J   w W

k K   x X

l L   y Y

m M   z Z

Dictionary resource sheet 3

x X

_____

y Y

year

yellow

yes

you

your

z Z

zip

- -

a A

a	animals
able	another
about	anyway
address	apple
afraid	are
after	arm
again	as
alarm	at
alien	autumn
all	away
am	
an	
and	

Dictionary resource sheet 4

b B

back

ball

banana

battery

be

because

bed

been

big

bite

biting

black

blue

boat

bonfire

both

boy

branch

break

breakfast

brick

brother

brown

bulb

bungalow

but

by

w W

Wales

want

was

water

way

we

week

went

were

west

what

when

where

white

who

will

window

winter

wire

with

woke

wood

would

Dictionary resource sheet 5

c C

call	chin
called	colour
came	come
can	comes
canines	coming
can't	could
caravan	country
cat	countries
caught	cricket
cereals	
chase	
cheek	
chew	

v V

vegetables

very

Dictionary resource sheet 6

d D

dad _____

dark _____

day _____

did _____

dig _____

do _____

dog _____

don't _____

door _____

down _____

downstairs _____

dressed _____

drove _____

u U

under _____

United Kingdom _____

until _____

up _____

upstairs _____

us _____

Dictionary resource sheet 7

t T

take _____

tail _____

teacher _____

teeth _____

tenth _____

than _____

thank _____

that _____

the _____

their _____

them _____

then _____

there _____

these _____

they _____

third _____

this _____

three _____

through _____

tile _____

time _____

to _____

tongue _____

too _____

took _____

tooth _____

towards _____

trap _____

trapping _____

tree _____

trunk _____

trust _____

two _____

_____

_____

e E

ear _____

earlobe _____

early _____

east _____

eleventh _____

England _____

evening _____

ever _____

every _____

eye _____

eyebrow _____

eyelashes _____

_____

Dictionary resource sheet 8

f F

fable

face

favourite

fifth

fire

fireworks

first

flat

flew

flower

foot

football

for

four

fourth

friendly

from

front

fruit

s S

safe

said

saw

school

Scotland

second

see

seen

seven

seventh

she

should

shower

sister

sixth

sleep

slow

slowly

so

some

south

space

spring

starts

stem

summer

swoop

Dictionary resource sheet 9

g G

garden
_____

gave
_____

get
_____

girl
_____

glass
_____

go
_____

goes
_____

going
_____

good
_____

got
_____

green
_____

ground
_____

growing
_____

r R

ran
_____

red
_____

really
_____

roar
_____

roof
_____

roots
_____

rope
_____

Dictionary resource sheet 10

h H

had

hair

half

halfway

has

have

he

heard

help

her

here

hide

him

his

hobbies

hobby

holiday

home

house

how

huge

hunting

hurry

q Q

quick

quickly

quiet

quietly

quite

Dictionary resource sheet 11

p P

people

pineapple

pink

place

play

please

pot

promise

protect

pull

purple

push

put

i I

I

if

in

incisors

is

it

Dictionary resource sheet 12

j J

juice

jump

just

o O

o'clock

of

off

old

on

once

one

only

or

orange

our

out

over

owl

Dictionary resource sheet 13

n N

name

near

neck

new

next

night

ninth

no

north

Northern Ireland

nose

nostril

not

now

k K

kill

knew

know

Dictionary resource sheet 14

l L

ladder _____

last _____

late _____

later _____

laugh _____

leaf _____

leap _____

leaves _____

leg _____

letterbox _____

like _____

lion _____

lip _____

little _____

live _____

lived _____

look _____

loud _____

loudly _____

love _____

m M

made _____

make _____

man _____

many _____

may _____

me _____

molars _____

moral _____

more _____

morning _____

mouse _____

mouth _____

much _____

mum _____

must _____

my _____